ISBN: 978-0-9813499-5-4

Printed in Canada by: Friesens Corporation

Peer-reviewed by: Anaar Bhopa, MD CCFP and, Sheriffa Bhopa, ND

A. A. Smith Publishing House
Whitchurch-Stouffville, Ontario
Visit us at www.aasmithpublishing.com

Dedication

This book has been peer-reviewed by my naturopath mother and
physician sister.
These inspiring women taught me about the gut-brain connection,
and how mindfulness can change your life.
The main characters in this book are emulated after my sweet nephew Ayan and
his physician mom, Anaar.

Shania Bhopa MSc
Anaar Bhopa MD CCFP
Sheriffa Bhopa ND

Because wellness is balance and balance is wellness.

Gurk & Bianca

Shania Bhopa

Meet Gurk the gut: he is courageous, hardworking and a natural born leader.

Meet Bianca the brain: she is smart, shy and determined.

These body buddies talk all day long!

From conversations about the human's homework, to discussing their human's feelings,

the two chat about everything and anything!

2

Sometimes when Bianca has too much work to do, she relies on her best friend Gurk to help her feel better.

And most of the time Gurk does a pretty good job!

"Oh no, do you hear that?"
Bianca asked Gurk.

"Our human came home
from school with
a tummy ache!" Gurk said.

4

"Let's figure out if our human's tummy ache is physical."

"It looks like it doesn't hurt our human…" Bianca said.

5

"Hmmm, it seems like our human is feeling a lot of different emotions. Can you help me figure out what's wrong Gurk? We need to make our human feel better," Bianca pleaded.

"I have a few ideas of what we can do to make our human feel better!" Gurk replied.

"Let's try having our human hang out at the park with his pals," Bianca suggested.

"Oh yippee Bianca! Our human always feels happiest when he's with his pals!" Gurk agreed.

"Oh no, our human isn't having any fun at the park!" Gurk frowned.

8

"Let's see if our human might be thirsty – warm water always makes our human feel better."

Ouch my tummy still hurts

9

"Oh, I have an idea!" Bianca exclaimed. "Maybe we should give our human something to eat like colourful soup?"

"That's a great idea!" Gurk agreed. "We can even add his favourite vegetables and noodles."

"It's a good idea to eat some soup and...

"Check the poop!"
Gurk and Bianca say in unison.

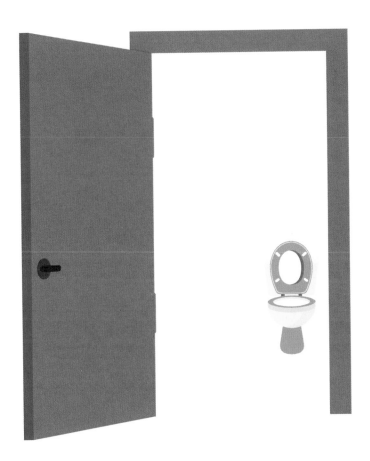

Still no luck

"Wait a second, we forgot about the special juice!" said Gurk.

Bianca watched nervously, "I really hope this works.
One tablespoon usually seems to do the trick!"

12

"Gurk, why aren't we having ANY luck? Maybe we should give up."

"Bianca, we can't give up, he is our human! It is our job to make sure he feels good."

13

"There's one thing we have not tried. Let's ask mom!" Bianca said.

14

"Mom! My tummy
has been
hurting all day,"
our human said.

"Oh no honey, I am going to check your temperature and gently press on your tummy to see if you have any specific pain."

"Okay your temperature is good, and you have no pain, is it just an uncomfortable feeling?"

"Sometimes this discomfort can be from how your body digests food. The way we feel, like sadness, jealousy and anger, can affect digestion... Maybe this has something to do with your tummy ache?"

18

"Remember yesterday when you were playing with your favourite toy and that's all you wanted to do for an hour? You were paying full attention. Now do the same thing – but this time with your feelings. This focus means you are being mindful," Mom said.

"**Mindfulness means paying full attention to something.**

It means slowing down to hear your thoughts, and taking the time to understand how they make you feel.

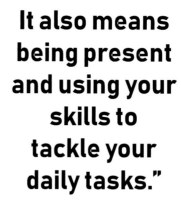

It also means being present and using your skills to tackle your daily tasks."

"So let's breathe in, and breathe out and think about how we feel. Mindfulness should be practiced every day, to help tummy aches, loosy poops before presentations, and sad tears."

21

"Let's start with mindful
breathing."

"Breathe in
1, 2, 3
and breathe out
1, 2, 3,"
Mom chanted.

Human begins his body scan from his nose to his toes

23

"We did it Gurk! The key to feeling better is mindfulness."

"Mindfulness helps us understand that everything our human puts into his body, from thoughts to food, can affect how our human's mind and body feel."

"The key to this, Bianca, is to make sure our human is aware of every emotion. When our human can talk through his feelings, it means those feelings will not stay bottled up and make our human sick."

"And we cannot forget about eating colourful whole foods and engaging in nature."

"Sometimes just a five-minute walk or sitting down to think about your day can make all the difference!"

"Because what affects you, affects me, Gurk."

"And what affects you, affects me, Bianca."

Be mindful humans, see you next time!

Mindfulness Activity
Journal Prompts

Take this time with your child to unravel the association between Gurk the Gut and Bianca the Brain when they feel:

1. Nervous before a presentation
2. Jealous, fearful or distant in a friendship, causing stress
3. Anxious in a social gathering

Mindfulness Awareness Practice is an exercise to promote a state of heightened and receptive attention to moment-by-moment experiences.

Answer these questions at the end of every day:

1. Today I feel...
2. Today I am grateful for...
3. What was a moment you had to stop and think?
4. How did your food fuel you today?

Breathe. Reflect. Be Mindful.

Notes From the Author

As a child, I had a hard time understanding my emotions, focusing my thoughts and voicing my feelings to my parents. I did not understand how I was feeling, and why my digestion was a bit off when I was stressed, sad, angry or frustrated. I had no idea why I felt a heavy pain in my chest in the mornings or why I could never sleep at night. It felt unfair - it felt limiting. Despite having a naturopath as a mom and a physician as a sister, most of my time was spent at school and the education on well-being was lacking.

It wasn't until my teen years that I recognized the connection between the mind and the gut. When looking towards the literature, and learning from my mom and my sister I created a new habit. Instead of asking myself, "What did I eat to cause this feeling?" I replaced it with "How do I feel in this situation". Realizing that my environment and my racing thoughts had a part to play in my digestion and overall well-being.

I learned that, in many cases, our emotions can impact our digestive health. Even though I was nourishing my body with the "right" nutrients, I learned that I needed to fuel my mind, body, and soul for overall well-being. It wasn't until I practiced mindfulness that I discovered strategies to cope with everyday stressors and nourish my mind.

Mindfulness allowed me to be the person I had always dreamed of being.

 @wellbyshaniabhopa

But what IS mindfulness?

Mindfulness isn't learned overnight.

Mindfulness promotes focus and cognitive control which are controlled in the prefrontal cortex.

Mindfulness can promote the development of skills including self-regulation, judgment, and problem-solving during childhood.

People who practice mindfulness typically have higher levels of self-esteem, emotional intelligence and self-perception.

This is directly associated with greater resilience and less negative self-talk.

Mindfulness is a skill just like ice skating or walking.

And WHAT is the gut-brain connection?

Most of the controls asserted by the parasympathetic nervous system run through the vagus nerve- the main communication portal through which the gut and brain connect. The bi-directional communication between the brain and the gastrointestinal tract, the "brain–gut axis," is based on a complex system. Our gut microbiome is sensitive to the foods we consume to fuel our bodies, and factors such as our environment, genetics, age and lifestyle contribute to our overall gut health. We need to begin to fuel our bodies with nutrients, positive self-talk, hydration, and care.

We have all experienced the connection between our mind and our gut—the choices we made because it "*felt right*"; the butterflies in our stomach before a big meeting; the anxious stomach rumbling we get when we are experiencing stress. While the research on the gut-brain connection is up-and coming, the goal of Gurk and Bianca's story is to promote a child's awareness of how their entire body is interconnected.

My story learning about the gut-brain connection began in 2017 after a year of excruciating digestive pain every moment of every day. My mother Sheriffa, a naturopath, and sister Anaar, a physician, changed my life. They helped me see how emotions and stress *physically* affected the way that I digested food. My mother emphasized how we all as humans live under vast amounts of stress, and our bodies do not know how to adequately distinguish between different *types* of stressors. My sister emphasized that the food you eat not only needs to be good for your health but also for your gut microbiome.

My mother and sister taught me how important it is to really see your body as an interconnected unit, in which all avenues from immunity to digestion, to brain health affect one another at all moments of the day. I learned how to take a step back and instead of analyzing a system in isolation, I thought more holistically. I chose to pursue lifestyle changes to improve my digestion, working on my relationship with food, mindful eating and daily meditation to allow my body to process stress.

I believe that changing the way that we frame wellness starts with our children. We must take responsibility over our health, and it starts by using the tools in our very own lives to learn how to manage our stressors. I wrote "Gurk and Bianca" to help children explore the gut-brain relationship and introduce the role of mindfulness. Promoting **mindfulness** is a holistic way to empower youth to reflect on their sense of self, build confidence and monitor their own health.

I hope that parents and children alike will be able to engage in habits that foster mindfulness.

Because balance is wellness & *wellness is balance.*

Shania Bhopa

Mindfulness
begins
with you.

Shania Bhopa

You are a beautiful human!

Shania Bhopa

About the Author

No child's health should be left up to chance.

Shania Bhopa, BA, MSc

Shania Bhopa is a second-generation Canadian, born and raised just outside of Toronto. A highly recognized public speaker and humanitarian, Shania has focused her early career on child mental health and strategic communications. Bhopa is co-founder and executive director of The Canadian Courage Project, a non-profit organization striving to support the mental health of youth facing homelessness, and empowering youth to take action in their community. With a true passion for health literacy, knowledge translation, and global health, Bhopa hopes to have every young person in the world feel empowered about their wellness and strive to be the best they can be.

Gurk and Bianca is the world's first children's book to introduce the gut-brain connection in a thought-provoking sequence. Bhopa presents the power of mindfulness on the body, mind, and soul and bases the story on holistic health and balanced living. Gurk and Bianca is the analogy every child needs to take with them.

Wellness is balance and balance is wellness.

@wellbyshaniabhopa

Made in the USA
Monee, IL
18 February 2022

91427040R00026